LOST AND FOUND

Florence Parry Heide
Sylvia Worth Van Clief

Senior Authors
Carl B. Smith
Ronald Wardhaugh

Macmillan Publishing Co., Inc.
New York

Collier Macmillan Publishers
London

SERIES **r**
Macmillan Reading

ACKNOWLEDGMENTS

The publisher gratefully acknowledges permission to reprint the following copyrighted material:

"The Balloon Man" by Larry Kirkman from *Zoo! A Book of Poems* selected by Lee Bennett Hopkins. Copyright © 1971 by Larry Kirkman. Reprinted by permission of Larry Kirkman.

Illustrations: Ray Cruz, pp. 2-3; Blaire Drawson, pp. 4-13; John Wallner, pp. 26-27; Len Ebert, pp. 28-37; Burt Groedel, pp. 38-39; Allan Eitzen, pp. 42-53; Rita Genet, pp. 54-61. **Photographs:** James Foote and Michael Gold, pp. 14-25. **Cover Design:** AKM Associates

Parts of this work were published in SERIES r: The New Macmillan Reading Program.

Macmillan Publishing Co., Inc.
866 Third Avenue, New York, New York 10022
Collier Macmillan Canada, Ltd.

Printed in the United States of America
ISBN 0-02-128260-9
98765432

Contents

Where Are You?

Kim runs to see Kate.

"Where are you, Kate?"
calls Kim.

"In the house," says Kate.

So Kim runs in
to see Kate.
And Kate runs out
to see Kim.

But Kim can't see Kate.
And Kate can't see Kim.

9

"Where are you, Kim?"
calls Kate.
"In the house," says Kim.

So Kate runs in
to see Kim.
And Kim runs out
to see Kate.

But Kim can't see Kate.
And Kate can't see Kim.

11

A man rides up
to the house.
The boys and girls run
to the man.

Kim and Kate run, too.

Kim sees Kate.
And Kate sees Kim.

BLAIR DRAWSON

I Like the City

I like to walk
in the city.
I can see funny things
in the city.

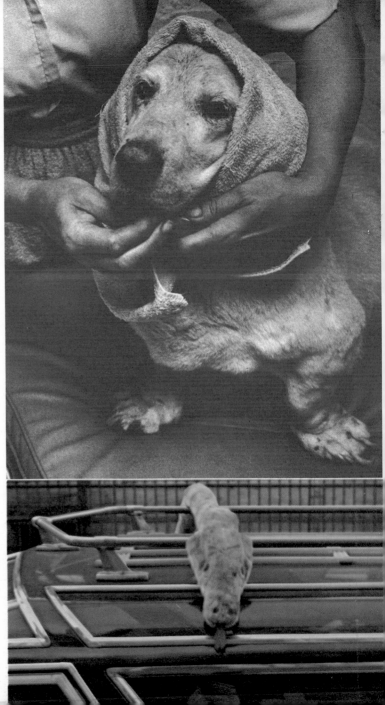

What can you see
in the city?

18

I like to ride the bus.
I can see funny things
in the bus.
What can you see
in the bus?

19

I like to walk in the park.
I can see funny things in the park.

20

What can you see in the park?

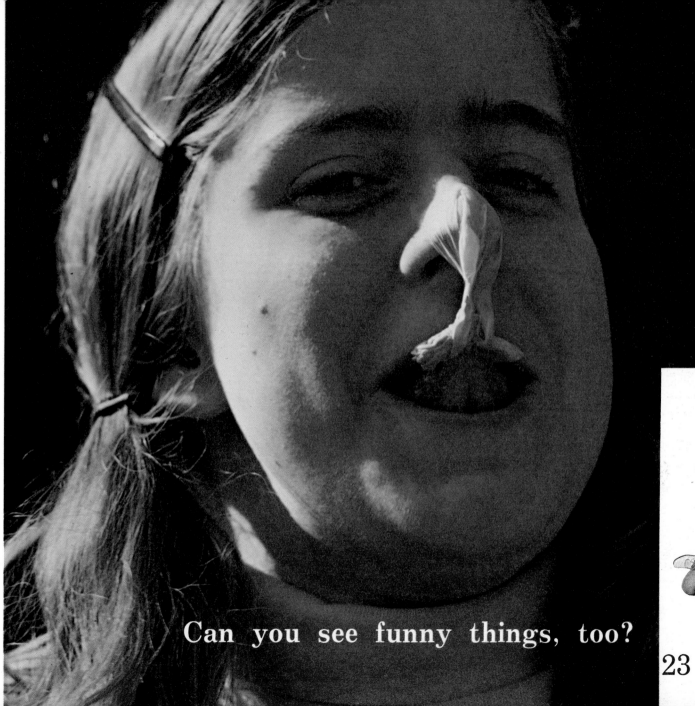

Can you see funny things, too?

23

THE BALLOON MAN

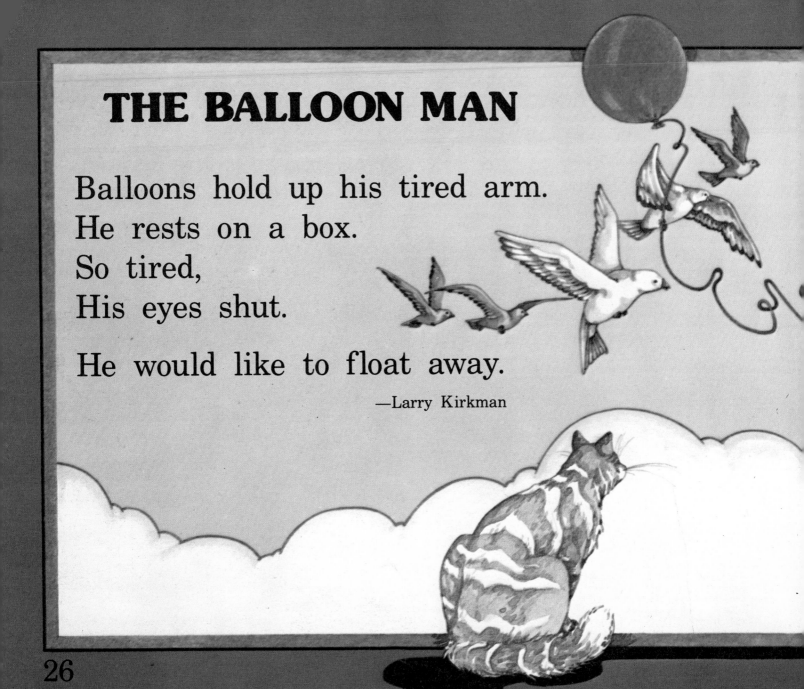

Balloons hold up his tired arm.
He rests on a box.
So tired,
His eyes shut.

He would like to float away.

—Larry Kirkman

LOST

28

I like to ride my pony.
I ride to the lake.
My pony can walk
in the lake.

I see a hill.
I ride up the hill.
I look down.
I see the woods.

I ride my pony
down the hill.
I ride my pony
in the woods.

32

I see a hill.
I ride up the hill.
I look down.
I see the woods.

31

I ride my pony
down the hill.
I ride my pony
in the woods.

32

I can't see the hill.
I can't see the lake.
I can't see my house.
My pony and I are lost.

We ride and ride
in the woods.
Where are we?
We are lost.

34

I see my dog.
My dog runs.
I ride out of the woods.

I can see the hill.
I can see the lake.
I can see my house.

36

And I ride home.

BUTTERFLY

The butterfly
Is not a bird.
To say he is
Would be absurd.
He does have wings
And flies a lot,
But a bird is something he is not.

Doing Words

He can walk.
Can you walk?

He can jump.
Can you jump?

He can run.
Can you run?

He can fly.
Can you fly?

He can ride.
Can you ride?

You can read.
Can he read?

What can you do?

42

I Can't Fly

44

The big birds fly
up the hill.
The little bird sits.

"Fly, little bird,"
says a big bird.

"I can't fly,"
says the little bird.
"But I can walk."

So the little bird walks
up the hill.
And the little bird walks
down the hill.

46

The big birds fly
to the city.

"Fly, little bird,"
says a big bird.

"I can't fly,"
says the little bird.
"But I can run."

So the little bird runs
to the city.

The big birds fly
to the boy.

"Fly, little bird,"
says a big bird.

"I can't fly,"
says the little bird.
"But I can jump."

51

So the little bird jumps

and jumps

and jumps!

"I can fly!"
says the little bird.

And the little bird and
the big birds fly home.

53

54

You

Are you a boy
or a girl?
Are you big
or little?
Who are **you**?

Who is in your family?
Is your family
big or little?
Who is in your family?

What is
your house like?
Is your house
little or big?
What is
your house like?

58

Where do you live?
Do you live in a city?
Or do you live
in the woods?

Where do you live?

Boy or girl,
big or little,
you are **you**.

That is who you are.

Where is the girl?

What does he see?

Who is the girl?

63

WORD LIST

4. where	19. bus	41. fly
are	20. park	*do*
6. Kim	28. lost	45. birds
see	30. my	*bird*
Kate	pony	*sits*
13. *sees*	lake	46. *walks*
15. city	31. woods	56. or
16. funny	34. we	57. your
things	37. home	family
17. what	40. doing	59. live
	words	

To the Teacher: The words listed beside the page numbers above are introduced in *Lost and Found*, Level 5 of SERIES r. The children should be able to use previously taught skills to identify the italicized words independently.